digital

With digital materials

Including Festival lessons (**Halloween, Christmas, Easter**)

macmillan education

Claire Medwell

Course consultant: Sandie Mourão

Macmillan Education
4 Crinan Street
London N1 9XW
A division of Springer Nature Limited

Companies and representatives throughout the world

ISBN 978-0-230-44693-9

Written by Claire Medwell

First published 2015

Original design by Anthony Godber
Page make-up by Carolyn Gibson
Original character concept by Mike Brownlow
Illustrated by Pablo Gallego (Beehive Illustration)
Additional artwork provided by Aleksandar Sotirovski (Beehive Illustration), Tamara Joubert (Beehive Illustration)
Cover design by Macmillan Publishers Limited and Astwood Design Consultancy
Cover illustration by Pablo Gallego (Beehive Illustration)

Authors' acknowledgements
With special thanks to all of the Macmillan team and to Sandie Mourão for all of her invaluable input and support.

The publishers would like to thank
Asunción Morcillo Escudero, CEIP Leonardo Torres Quevedo, Coslada, Madrid; Beverly Round, Colegio Lope de Vega, Benidorm, Alicante; Carolina Marcos, Colegio Nuestra Señora de Loreto, Madrid; Esther Rodríguez Velasco, CEIP Campomaior, Ordes, A Coruña; Gema Morante Montero, Centro Cultural Salmantino, Madrid; Isabel Melcón Pérez, Colegio La Purísima, Madrid; María Torres Sanz, Colegio Nuestra Señora de la Merced, Madrid; María del Mar Cano Mesa, Col·legi Maristes de Sant Josep, Badalona, Barcelona; Mercedes Peinado Sánchez, CEIP Conde de Arruga, Madrid; Mónica Vicente García, CEIP Pinar del Rey, Madrid; Olga Martí Frigolé, Escola Sala i Badrinas, Terrasa, Barcelona; Teresa Paredes Andrés, Madrid; Yolanda Neira Gómez, CRA Boqueixón-Vedra, Lestedo, A Coruña.

Printed and bound in China

2020 2019
20 19 18

1 Discover my family

Vocabulary lesson

1 Discover my family

Name: ______________________

1: Vocabulary lesson

Pupil's Book worksheet *page 3*

CD1 13 CD1 14 **I Love My Family song**

I love Mummy! *I do, I do* *I love Mummy!* *Yes, I do!*	*I love Brother!* *I do, I do* *I love Brother!* *Yes, I do!*
I love Daddy! *I do, I do* *I love Daddy!* *Yes, I do!*	*I love Sister!* *I do, I do* *I love Sister!* *Yes, I do!*

- Stick the stickers in the correct place.
- Point to the family members and say the words.
- Trace the lines to match.
- Colour the family members.
- Sing *I Love My Family* and point to the family members.

digital **Teacher's Presentation Kit for Unit 1**

Personalisation Discover for yourself

Extra activity Draw your family.

1 Discover my family

Name: ____________________

2: Story lesson

Pupil's Book worksheet *page 5*

CD1 15 **Hello Dex story**

- Point to the family members and say the words.
- Colour Dex.
- Colour the ball.

3: Concepts lesson

Photocopiable worksheet *Teacher's Book page 138*

- Point to the sun and the rain and say *sunny* or *rainy*.
- Colour the sun.
- Colour the rain.

1 Discover my family

Name: ______________________

4: Colours and numbers lesson

Pupil's Book worksheet *page 7*

CD1 16 CD1 17 **One Red Heart song**

One red heart
One red heart
I have one red heart
One red heart!

- Trace the heart.
- Colour the heart red.
- Point and say *one red heart*.
- Sing *One Red Heart* and point to the heart.

5: Kid's culture lesson

Photocopiable worksheet *Teacher's Book page 139*

CD1 18 CD1 19 **Family Fingers nursery rhyme**

Daddy finger, Daddy finger
Where are you?
Here I am! Here I am!
How are you?

Mummy finger, Mummy finger
Where are you?
Here I am! Here I am!
How are you?

Brother finger, Brother finger
Where are you?
Here I am! Here I am!
How are you?

Sister finger, Sister finger
Where are you?
Here I am! Here I am!
How are you?

Dex finger, Dex finger
Where are you?
Here I am! Here I am!
How are you?

- Point to the family members and say the words.
- Trace the lines to match the family members to the fingers.
- Colour the family members.
- Sing *Family Fingers* and point to the family members.

6: Review lesson

Photocopiable worksheet *Teacher's Book page 140*

- Circle the family members.
- Point to the family members and say the words.
- Colour the picture.

7: PLUS vocabulary lesson / Extension

Photocopiable worksheet *Teacher's Book page 141*

CD1 21 CD1 22 **I Love My Family PLUS song**

- Fold along the dotted lines to make a wordbook. First, fold backwards along the horizontal line.
- Then, fold backwards along the right vertical line, and fold forwards along the left vertical line.
- Point to the family members in the wordbook and say the words.
- Colour the pictures.

2 Discover my classroom
Vocabulary lesson

2 Discover my classroom

Name: ______________________________

1: Vocabulary lesson

Pupil's Book worksheet *page 9*

CD1 24 CD1 25 **This Is My Classroom song**

Look, look!
This is my book
Open, open my book

Look, look!
This is my crayon
Draw, draw with my crayon

Look, look!
This is my table
Tap, tap my table

Look, look!
This is my chair
Sit, sit on my chair

- Stick the stickers in the correct place.
- Point to the classroom objects and say the words.
- Trace the lines to match.
- Colour the classroom objects.
- Sing *This Is My Classroom* and point to the classroom objects.

digital **Teacher's Presentation Kit for Unit 2**

Personalisation Discover for yourself

Extra activity Draw your classroom.

2 Discover my classroom

Name: ______________________________

2: Story lesson

Pupil's Book worksheet *page 11*

CD1 26 **Where's My Crayon? story**

- Point to the book and the crayon and say the words.
- Trace the leaf.
- Colour the leaf yellow.

3: Concepts lesson

Photocopiable worksheet *Teacher's Book page 142*

- Point to the weather and say *cloudy* or *windy*.
- Trace the cloud.
- Colour the cloud and the wind.

2 Discover my classroom

Name: ______________________

4: Colours and numbers lesson

Pupil's Book worksheet *page 13*

CD1 27 CD1 28 **Two Yellow Leaves song**

One yellow leaf
Falling, falling, falling

Two yellow leaves
Falling, falling, falling

One yellow leaf
Falling, falling, falling

Two yellow leaves
Falling to the ground

- Point to one leaf and say *one*.
- Point to two leaves and say *two*.
- Trace the lines to match the leaves to the trees.
- Colour the leaves yellow.
- Sing *Two Yellow Leaves* and point to the leaves.

Personalisation Discover for yourself

Extra activity Draw your favourite weather.

2 Discover my classroom

Name: ______________________

5: Kid's culture lesson

Pupil's Book worksheet *page 15*

CD1 29 CD1 30 **Rain, Rain, Go Away nursery rhyme**

Rain, rain, go away
Come again another day
Mummy wants to play

Rain, rain, go away
Come again another day
Daddy wants to play

Rain, rain, go away
Come again another day
Brother wants to play

Rain, rain, go away
Come again another day
Sister wants to play

Rain, rain, go away
Come again another day
Everybody wants to play

- Point to the family members and say the words.
- Point to the pictures and say *rainy* or *sunny*.
- Trace the frame around the rainy picture.
- Colour the frame around the sunny picture yellow.
- Sing *Rain, Rain, Go Away* and point to the rainy picture.

6: Review lesson

Photocopiable worksheet *Teacher's Book page 143*

- Circle the classroom objects.
- Point to the classroom objects and say the words.
- Colour the picture.

7: PLUS vocabulary lesson / Extension

Photocopiable worksheet *Teacher's Book page 144*

CD1 32 CD1 33 **This Is My Classroom PLUS song**

- Fold along the dotted lines to make a wordbook. First, fold backwards along the horizontal line.
- Then, fold backwards along the right vertical line, and fold forwards along the left vertical line.
- Point to the classroom objects in the wordbook and say the words.
- Colour the pictures.

3 Discover toys

Vocabulary lesson

3 Discover toys

Name: ____________________

1: Vocabulary lesson

Pupil's Book worksheet *page 17*

CD1 35 CD1 36 **My Favourite Toys song**

Rock, rock my doll
Rock, rock my doll

Hug, hug my teddy
Hug, hug my teddy

Bounce, bounce my ball
Bounce, bounce my ball

Vroom, vroom my car
Vroom, vroom my car

- Stick the stickers in the correct place.
- Point to the toys and say the words.
- Circle your favourite toy.
- Colour Dex.
- Sing *My Favourite Toys* and point to the toys.

digital **Teacher's Presentation Kit for Unit 3**

Personalisation Discover for yourself

Extra activity Draw your favourite toy.

3 Discover toys

Name: ______________________________

2: Story lesson

Pupil's Book worksheet *page 19*

CD1 37 **Let's Tidy Up! story**

- Point to the characters and say their names.
- Point to the toys and say the words.
- Trace the lines to match the characters to their favourite toys.
- Colour the toys.

3: Concepts lesson

Photocopiable worksheet *Teacher's Book page 145*

- Point to the pictures and say *tidy* or *messy*.
- Colour the frame around the tidy picture yellow.
- Colour the frame around the messy picture red.

3 Discover toys

Name: ______________________________

4: Colours and numbers lesson

Pupil's Book worksheet *page 21*

CD1 38 CD1 39 **Three Blue Balls song**

One blue ball
Up in the air

Two blue balls
Up in the air

Three blue balls
Up in the air

One, two, three
Fall down!

- Count the balls and say the number.
- Trace the ball.
- Colour the balls blue.
- Point to the balls and say *three blue balls*.
- Sing *Three Blue Balls* and point to the balls.

Personalisation Discover for yourself

Extra activity Draw something blue.

3 Discover toys

Name: ______________________________

5: Kid's culture lesson

Pupil's Book worksheet *page 23*

CD1 40 CD1 41 **Teddy Bear, Teddy Bear nursery rhyme**

Teddy bear, teddy bear
Turn around
Teddy bear, teddy bear
Touch the ground

Teddy bear, teddy bear
Touch your toes
Teddy bear, teddy bear
Wiggle your nose

Teddy bear, teddy bear
Nod your head
Teddy bear, teddy bear
Go to bed

Teddy bear, teddy bear
Close your eyes
Teddy bear, teddy bear
Say 'Goodnight'

- Point to the teddies.
- Draw lines to match the teddies to Meg.
- Colour the teddies.
- Sing *Teddy Bear, Teddy Bear* and point to the teddies.

6: Review lesson

Photocopiable worksheet *Teacher's Book page 146*

- Circle the toys.
- Point to the toys and say the words.
- Colour the picture.

7: PLUS vocabulary lesson / Extension

Photocopiable worksheet *Teacher's Book page 147*

CD2 43 CD2 44 **My Favourite Toys PLUS song**

- Fold along the dotted lines to make a wordbook. First, fold backwards along the horizontal line.
- Then, fold backwards along the right vertical line, and fold forwards along the left vertical line.
- Point to the toys in the wordbook and say the words.
- Colour the pictures.

4 Discover my face

Vocabulary lesson

4 Discover my face

Name: ______________________________

1: Vocabulary lesson

Pupil's Book worksheet *page 25*

CD1 46 CD1 47 **My Face song**

Two eyes to see *Two eyes to see* *Like this!*	*One nose to smell* *One nose to smell* *Like this!*
Two ears to hear *Two ears to hear* *Like this!*	*One mouth to eat* *One mouth to eat* *Like this!*

- Stick the stickers in the correct place.
- Point to the parts of the face and say the words.
- Draw lines to match the parts of the face to Meg.
- Trace Meg.
- Sing *My Face* and point to the parts of the face.

digital **Teacher's Presentation Kit for Unit 4**

Personalisation Discover for yourself

Extra activity Draw your face. Draw your eyes, ears, nose and mouth.

4 Discover my face

Name: ______________________

2: Story lesson

Pupil's Book worksheet *page 27*

CD1 48 **Cloud Faces story**

- Point to the characters and say their names.
- Point to the parts of the face in the cloud and say the words.
- Trace the cloud.
- Colour the clouds.

Being curious

3: Concepts lesson

Photocopiable worksheet *Teacher's Book page 148*

- Point to the parts of the face and say *big* or *small*.
- Point to the characters and say their names.
- Trace the lines to match the parts of the face to the characters.
- Colour the characters.

4 Discover my face

Name: ______________________________

4: Colours and numbers lesson

Pupil's Book worksheet *page 29*

CD1 49 CD1 50 **Four Green Dinosaurs song**

One green dinosaur
Stomp! Stomp! Stomp! Stomp!

Two green dinosaurs
Jump! Jump! Jump! Jump!

Three green dinosaurs
Walk! Walk! Walk! Walk!

Four green dinosaurs
Run! Run! Run! Run!

We all fall down!

- Count the dinosaurs and say the number.
- Trace the lines to match the dinosaurs to the shadows.
- Point to Dex and say his name.
- Circle Dex.
- Sing *Four Green Dinosaurs* and point to the dinosaurs.

Personalisation Discover for yourself

Extra activity Draw your favourite dinosaur from page 29.

Discover my face

Name: ______________________________

5: Kid's culture lesson

Pupil's Book worksheet *page 31*

CD1 51 CD1 52 **Two Little Eyes nursery rhyme**

Two little eyes to look around
Two little ears to hear each sound
One little nose to smell what's sweet
One little mouth that likes to eat

- Point to Charlie and say his name.
- Point to the parts of the face and say the words.
- Circle the parts of the face that are Charlie's.
- Colour the frame.
- Sing *Two Little Eyes* and point to Charlie's face.

6: Review lesson

Photocopiable worksheet *Teacher's Book page 149*

- Circle the parts of the face.
- Point to the parts of the face and say the words.
- Colour the picture.

7: PLUS vocabulary lesson / Extension

Photocopiable worksheet *Teacher's Book page 150*

CD1 54 CD1 55 **My Face PLUS song**

- Fold along the dotted lines to make a wordbook. First, fold backwards along the horizontal line.
- Then, fold backwards along the right vertical line, and fold forwards along the left vertical line.
- Point to the parts of the face in the wordbook and say the words.
- Colour the pictures.

5 Discover clothes
Vocabulary lesson

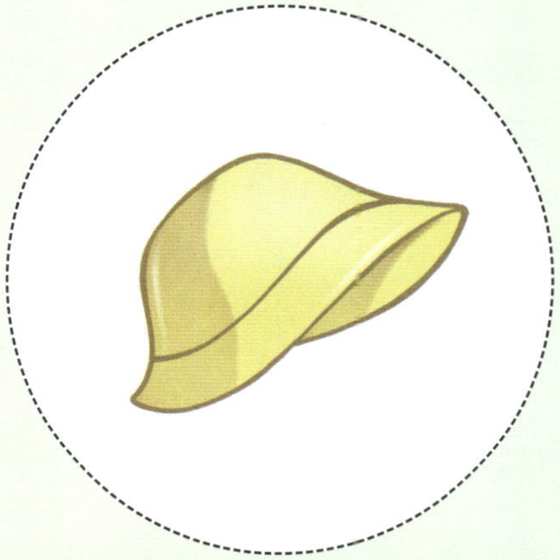
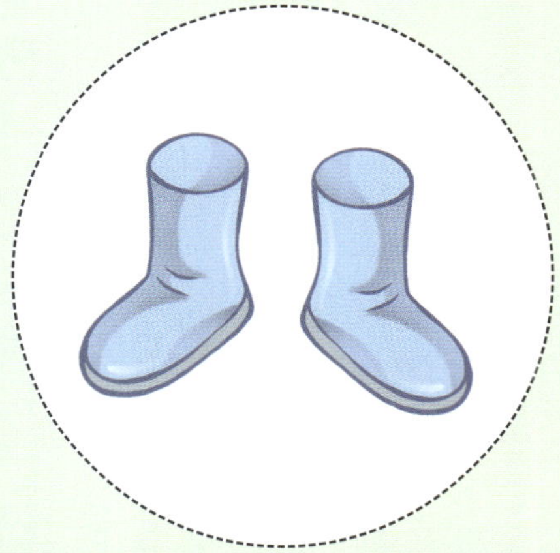

5 Discover clothes

Name: ____________________

1: Vocabulary lesson

Pupil's Book worksheet *page 33*

CD2 2 CD2 3 **My Clothes song**

Where's my coat?
Let's play!
Splish, splash, splosh!

Where's my hat?
Let's play!
Splish, splash, splosh!

Where are my boots?
Let's play!
Splish, splash, splosh!

Where's my umbrella?
It's rainy!

- Stick the stickers in the correct place.
- Point to the clothes and say the words.
- Find and circle the clothes in the puzzle.
- Match the clothes to the puzzle.
- Colour the clothes in the puzzle.
- Sing *My Clothes* and point to the clothes.

digital **Teacher's Presentation Kit for Unit 5**

Personalisation Discover for yourself

Extra activity Draw yourself wearing your favourite clothes.

5 Discover clothes

Name: ______________________________

2: Story lesson

Pupil's Book worksheet *page 35*

CD2 4 **A Rainy Day story**

- Point to the rain cloud and the sun and say *rainy* or *sunny*.
- Point to the clothes in the rainy picture and say the words.
- Draw lines to match the pictures to the sun or rain cloud.
- Colour the sun and the rain cloud.

3: Concepts lesson

Photocopiable worksheet *Teacher's Book page 151*

- Point to the characters and say their names.
- Point to the rain cloud and say *rainy*.
- Point to the characters and say *wet* or *dry*.
- Circle the wet characters.
- Colour the characters.

5 Discover clothes

Name: ______________________________

4: Colours and numbers lesson

Pupil's Book worksheet *page 37*

CD2 5 CD2 6 **Spotty Umbrellas song**

One red spot
One red spot
On my umbrella
One red spot
One
One red spot

Two blue spots
Two blue spots
On my umbrella
Two blue spots
One, two
Two blue spots

Three green spots
Three green spots
On my umbrella
Three green spots
One, two, three
Three green spots

Four yellow spots
Four yellow spots
On my umbrella
Four yellow spots
One, two, three, four
Four yellow spots

- Point to the umbrellas and say the colours.
- Count the spots on each character's umbrella and say the numbers.
- Trace the umbrellas.
- Circle the matching umbrellas in each row.
- Sing *Spotty Umbrellas* and point to the umbrellas.

Personalisation Discover for yourself

Extra activity Draw yourself holding a spotty umbrella.

5 Discover clothes

Name: ______________________________

5: Kid's culture lesson

Pupil's Book worksheet *page 39*

CD2 7 CD2 8 **Four Little Ducks nursery rhyme**

Four little ducks go out one day
Over the hill and far away
Mummy duck says 'Quack, quack, quack'
But only three little ducks come back

Three little ducks go out one day
Over the hill and far away
Mummy duck says 'Quack, quack, quack'
But only two little ducks come back

Two little ducks go out one day
Over the hill and far away
Mummy duck says 'Quack, quack, quack'
But only one little duck comes back

One little duck goes out one day
Over the hill and far away
Mummy duck says 'Quack, quack, quack'
And four little ducks come running back

- Count the ducks and say the number.
- Draw a line along the path to match the ducks to the pond.
- Colour the ducks.
- Sing *Four Little Ducks* and point to the ducks.

6: Review lesson

Photocopiable worksheet *Teacher's Book page 152*

- Circle the clothes.
- Point to the clothes and say the words.
- Colour the picture.

7: PLUS vocabulary lesson / Extension

Photocopiable worksheet *Teacher's Book page 153*

CD2 10 CD2 11 **My Clothes PLUS song**

- Fold along the dotted lines to make a wordbook. First, fold backwards along the horizontal line.
- Then, fold backwards along the right vertical line, and fold forwards along the left vertical line.
- Point to the clothes in the wordbook and say the words.
- Colour the pictures.

6 Discover food

Vocabulary lesson

6 Discover food

Name: ______________________________

1: Vocabulary lesson

Pupil's Book worksheet *page 41*

CD2 13 CD2 14 **My Favourite Food song**

I like biscuits
Yummy, yummy biscuits

I like biscuits
And yummy, yummy sandwiches

I like biscuits, sandwiches
And yummy, yummy bananas

I like biscuits, sandwiches, bananas
And yummy, yummy juice

- Stick the stickers in the correct place.
- Point to the food and say the words.
- Trace the table.
- Circle the food that you like.
- Sing *My Favourite Food* and point to the food.

digital **Teacher's Presentation Kit for Unit 6**

Personalisation Discover for yourself

Extra activity Draw your favourite food.

6 Discover food

Name: ____________________

2: Story lesson

Pupil's Book worksheet *page 43*

CD2 15 **Snack Time! story**

- Point to the characters and say their names.
- Follow the trail to find the biscuits.
- Who eats the biscuits in the story? Circle the characters.

Not being greedy

3: Concepts lesson

Photocopiable worksheet *Teacher's Book page 154*

- Point to Dex and say *hungry* or *thirsty*.
- Point to the food and say the words.
- Circle the food for hungry Dex and the drink for thirsty Dex.
- Colour the pictures.

6 Discover food

Name: ____________________

4: Colours and numbers lesson

Pupil's Book worksheet *page 45*

CD2 16 CD2 17 **Four Yummy Biscuits song**

Four biscuits on a plate
Four biscuits on a plate
Dex is hungry
Yum, yum, yum!

Three biscuits on a plate
Three biscuits on a plate
Buddy is hungry
Yum, yum, yum!

Two biscuits on a plate
Two biscuits on a plate
Dex is hungry
Yum, yum, yum!

One biscuit on a plate
One biscuit on a plate
Buddy is hungry
Yum, yum, yum!

- Count the biscuits and say the number.
- Follow the maze to match Dex and Buddy to the biscuits.
- Colour the biscuits.
- Sing *Four Yummy Biscuits* and point to the biscuits.

Personalisation Discover for yourself

Extra activity Draw four of your favourite biscuits.

6 Discover food

Name: ______________________________

5: Kid's culture lesson

Pupil's Book worksheet *page 47*

CD2 18 CD2 19 **Chick, Chick, Chick, Chick, Chicken nursery rhyme**

Chick, chick, chick, chick, chicken
Lay a little egg for me!
Chick, chick, chick, chick, chicken
I want one for me!

- Point to the food and say the words.
- Circle the egg.
- Draw a line to match the chicken to the egg.
- Colour the chicken.
- Sing *Chick, Chick, Chick, Chick, Chicken* and point to the chicken and the egg.

6: Review lesson

Photocopiable worksheet *Teacher's Book page 155*

- Circle the food.
- Point to the food and say the words.
- Colour the picture.

7: PLUS vocabulary lesson / Extension

Photocopiable worksheet *Teacher's Book page 156*

CD2 21 CD2 22 **My Favourite Food PLUS song**

- Fold along the dotted lines to make a wordbook. First, fold backwards along the horizontal line.
- Then, fold backwards along the right vertical line, and fold forwards along the left vertical line.
- Point to the food in the wordbook and say the words.
- Colour the pictures.

7 Discover animals

Vocabulary lesson

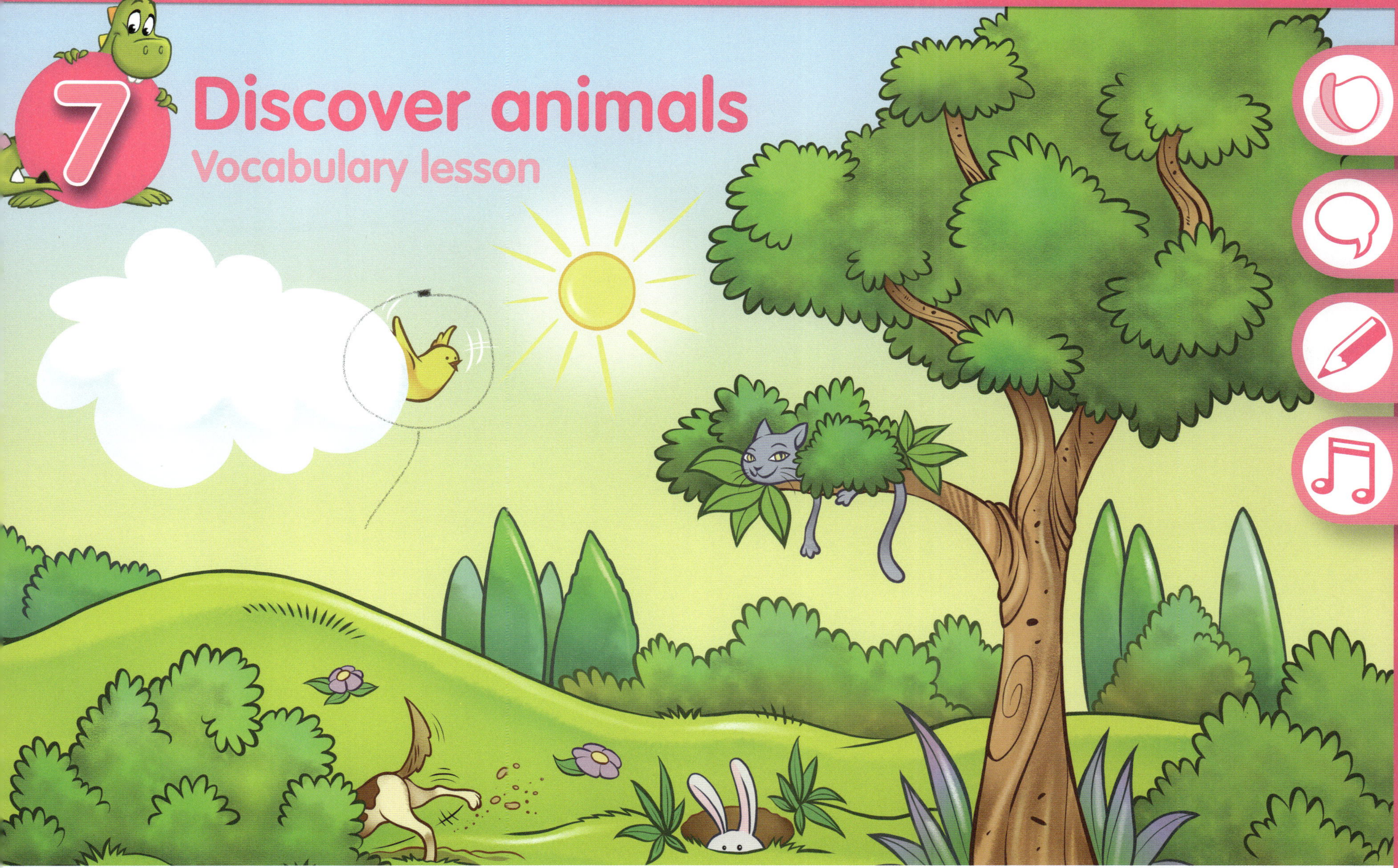

7 Discover animals

Name: ______________________

1: Vocabulary lesson

Pupil's Book worksheet *page 49*

CD2 24 CD2 25 **Animal Noises song**

It's a dog! It's a dog!
Woof, woof, woof
It's a dog!

It's a cat! It's a cat!
Miaow, miaow
It's a cat!

It's a bird! It's a bird!
Tweet, tweet, tweet
It's a bird!

It's a rabbit! It's a rabbit!
Munch, munch, munch
It's a rabbit!

Woof, miaow, tweet, munch!
Woof, miaow, tweet, munch!

- Stick the stickers in the correct place.
- Point to the animals and say the words.
- Find and circle the animals in the picture.
- Match the animals to the picture.
- Sing *Animal Noises* and point to the animals.

digital ➡ **Teacher's Presentation Kit for Unit 7**

Personalisation Discover for yourself

Extra activity Draw your favourite animal.

Buddy

7 Discover animals

Name: ______________________________

2: Story lesson

Pupil's Book worksheet *page 51*

CD2 26 **It's Bedtime! story**

- Point to the animals and say the words.
- Match each animal to its bed.
- Colour the animals.

Story value

Going to sleep at bedtime

3: Concepts lesson

Photocopiable worksheet *Teacher's Book page 157*

- Count the characters and say the number.
- Point to each character and say *tired* or *not tired*.
- Circle the tired characters.
- Colour the picture.

7 Discover animals

Name: ______________________________

4: Colours and numbers lesson

Pupil's Book worksheet *page 53*

CD2 27 CD2 28 **Four Little Birds song**

Four little birds sitting in a tree
One red bird
Says 'Play with me!'

Three little birds sitting in a tree
One yellow bird
Says 'Play with me!'

Two little birds sitting in a tree
One blue bird
Says 'Play with me!'

One little bird sitting in a tree
One green bird
Says 'Play with me!'

No little birds sitting in a tree
Now all the little birds are playing with me
Yippee!

- Count the birds and say the number.
- Trace the birds.
- Colour the first bird red, the second bird yellow, the third bird blue and the fourth bird green.
- Sing *Four Little Birds* and point to the birds.

Personalisation Discover for yourself

Extra activity Draw yourself under a colourful rainbow.

7 Discover animals

Name: ______________________

5: Kid's culture lesson

Pupil's Book worksheet *page 55*

CD2 29 CD2 30 **Twinkle, Twinkle, Little Star nursery rhyme**

Twinkle, twinkle, little star
How I wonder what you are
Up above the world so high
Like a diamond in the sky
Twinkle, twinkle, little star
How I wonder what you are

- Point to the stars and say *big* or *small*.
- Count the small stars and say the number.
- Trace the big star.
- Colour the big star.
- Sing *Twinkle, Twinkle, Little Star* and point to the stars.

6: Review lesson

Photocopiable worksheet *Teacher's Book page 158*

- Circle the animals.
- Point to the animals and say the words.
- Colour the picture.

7: PLUS vocabulary lesson / Extension

Photocopiable worksheet *Teacher's Book page 159*

CD2 32 CD2 33 **Animal Noises PLUS song**

- Fold along the dotted lines to make a wordbook. First, fold backwards along the horizontal line.
- Then, fold backwards along the right vertical line, and fold forwards along the left vertical line.
- Point to the animals in the wordbook and say the words.
- Colour the pictures.

8

Discover summer

Vocabulary lesson

8 Discover summer

Name: ______________________

1: Vocabulary lesson

Pupil's Book worksheet *page 57*

CD2 35 CD2 36 **Let's Swim! song**

Let's swim, let's swim, let's swim
Let's swim today!

Put on my cap
And my rubber ring

Let's swim, let's swim, let's swim
Let's swim today

Put on my armbands
And my goggles

Let's swim, let's swim, let's swim
Let's swim today

Let's swim, let's swim, let's swim
Have fun all day!

- Stick the stickers in the correct place.
- Point to the swimming objects and say the words.
- Draw lines to match the swimming objects to the correct part of Dex's body.
- Colour Dex's shorts.
- Sing *Let's Swim!* and point to the swimming objects.

digital **Teacher's Presentation Kit for Unit 8**

Personalisation Discover for yourself

Extra activity Draw yourself at the beach.

Story lesson 8

8 Discover summer

Name: ______________________________

2: Story lesson

Pupil's Book worksheet *page 59*

CD2 37 **Let's Swim! story**

- Point to the swimming objects and say the words.
- Circle the objects that Dex forgets in the story.
- Colour Dex.

3: Concepts lesson

Photocopiable worksheet *Teacher's Book page 160*

- Point to the pictures and say *hot* or *cold*.
- Colour the circles red for the hot pictures.
- Colour the circles blue for the cold pictures.

8 Discover summer

Name: ____________________

4: Colours and numbers lesson

Pupil's Book worksheet *page 61*

CD2 38 CD2 39 **Four Rubber Rings song**

A red rubber ring
In the sea, in the sea
The red rubber ring
Is for me, me, me!

A blue rubber ring
In the sea, in the sea
The blue rubber ring
Is for me, me, me!

A green rubber ring
In the sea, in the sea
The green rubber ring
Is for me, me, me!

A yellow rubber ring
In the sea, in the sea
The yellow rubber ring
Is for Buddy, Buddy, Buddy!

- Point to the swimming objects and say the words.
- Trace Dex's rubber ring.
- Colour Dex's rubber ring red, Charlie's rubber ring blue, Meg's rubber ring green and Buddy's rubber ring yellow.
- Sing *Four Rubber Rings* and point to the rubber rings.

Personalisation Discover for yourself

Extra activity Draw yourself in the sea with a rubber ring. Colour the rubber ring in your favourite colour.

8 Discover summer

Name: ______________________________

5: Kid's culture lesson

Pupil's Book worksheet *page 63*

CD2 40 CD2 41 **One Finger, One Thumb nursery rhyme**

One finger, one thumb, keep moving
One finger, one thumb, keep moving
One finger, one thumb, keep moving
We'll all be happy and play

One finger, one thumb, one arm, keep moving
One finger, one thumb, one arm, keep moving
One finger, one thumb, one arm, keep moving
We'll all be happy and play

One finger, one thumb, one arm, one leg, keep moving
One finger, one thumb, one arm, one leg, keep moving
One finger, one thumb, one arm, one leg, keep moving
We'll all be happy and play

One finger, one thumb, one arm, one leg, jump up and down, keep moving
One finger, one thumb, one arm, one leg, jump up and down, keep moving
One finger, one thumb, one arm, one leg, jump up and down, keep moving
We'll all be happy and play

- Point to the characters and say their names.
- Trace Meg's arm and Charlie's leg.
- Colour Dex.
- Sing *One Finger, One Thumb* and point to the picture.

6: Review lesson

Photocopiable worksheet *Teacher's Book page 161*

- Circle the swimming objects.
- Point to the swimming objects and say the words.
- Colour the picture.

7: PLUS vocabulary lesson / Extension

Photocopiable worksheet *Teacher's Book page 162*

CD2 43 CD2 44 **Let's Swim! PLUS song**

- Fold along the dotted lines to make a wordbook. First, fold backwards along the horizontal line.
- Then, fold backwards along the right vertical line, and fold forwards along the left vertical line.
- Point to the swimming objects in the wordbook and say the words.
- Colour the pictures.